P9-BIX-664

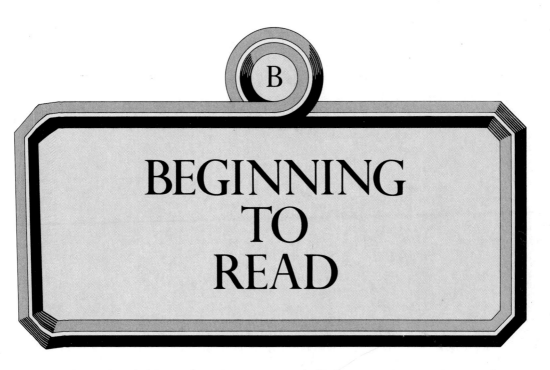

BEGINNING TO READ

HOUGHTON MIFFLIN LITERARY READERS

HOUGHTON MIFFLIN COMPANY   BOSTON

Atlanta   Dallas   Geneva, Illinois   Palo Alto   Princeton   Toronto

Program Authors

William K. Durr, John J. Pikulski, Rita M. Bean, J. David Cooper, Nicholas A. Glaser, M. Jean Greenlaw, Hugh Schoephoerster, Mary Lou Alsin, Kathryn Au, Rosalinda B. Barrera, Joseph E. Brzeinski, Ruth P. Bunyan, Jacqueline C. Comas, Frank X. Estrada, Robert L. Hillerich, Timothy G. Johnson, Pamela A. Mason, Joseph S. Renzulli

Senior Consultants

Jacqueline L. Chaparro, Alan N. Crawford, Alfredo Schifini, Sheila Valencia

Program Reviewers

Donna Bessant, Mara Bommarito, Yetive Bradley, Patricia M. Callan, Clara J. Hanline, Fannie Humphery, Barbara H. Jeffus, Beverly Jimenez, Sue Cramton Johnson, Michael P. Klentschy, Petra Montante, Nancy Rhodes, Julie Ryan, Lily Sarmiento, Ellis Vance, Judy Williams, Leslie M. Woldt, Janet Gong Yin

Acknowledgments

For each of the selections listed below, grateful acknowledgment is made for permission to adapt and/or reprint original or copyrighted material, as follows:

"Cat Goes Fiddle-i-fee," by Paul Galdone. Copyright © 1985 by Paul Galdone. Reprinted by permission of Clarion Books, a Houghton Mifflin company.

"Good Morning, Chick," written by Mirra Ginsburg and illustrated by Byron Barton. Copyright © 1980 by Mirra Ginsburg and Byron Barton. Reprinted by permission of Greenwillow Books, a division of William Morrow.

"A Kite," (anonymous) found in *Read-Aloud Rhymes for the Very Young*, edited by Jack Prelutsky. Copyright © 1986 by Alfred A. Knopf, Inc.

"The Little Turtle," from *Collected Poems* by Vachel Lindsay. Copyright © 1920 by Macmillan Publishing Company, renewed 1948 by Elizabeth C. Lindsay. Reprinted by permission of Macmillan Publishing Company.

"Over in the Meadow." Illustrations copyright © 1971 by Ezra Jack Keats. Reprinted by permission of Scholastic, Inc.

"Reading," from *Rhymes About Us* by Marchette Chute. Copyright © 1974 by Marchette Chute. Reprinted by permission of the author.

Credits

Illustrators: 4–5 Maxie Chambliss   **6** Carol Inouye   **7–28** Paul Galdone   **29–36** Marc Brown **37–52** Byron Barton   **53** Shelley Freshman   **54–62** David McPhail   **63–83** Ezra Jack Keats **84–85** Shelley Freshman   **86–95** James Marshall   **96** Nancy Winslow Parker

CDEFGHIJ-D-96543210/89

Contents

Say It Again!

Houghton Mifflin Literature
Oh, A–Hunting We Will Go

Say It Again!

5

Reading

by Marchette Chute

A story is a special thing.
　The ones that I have read,
They do not stay inside the books.
　They stay inside my head.

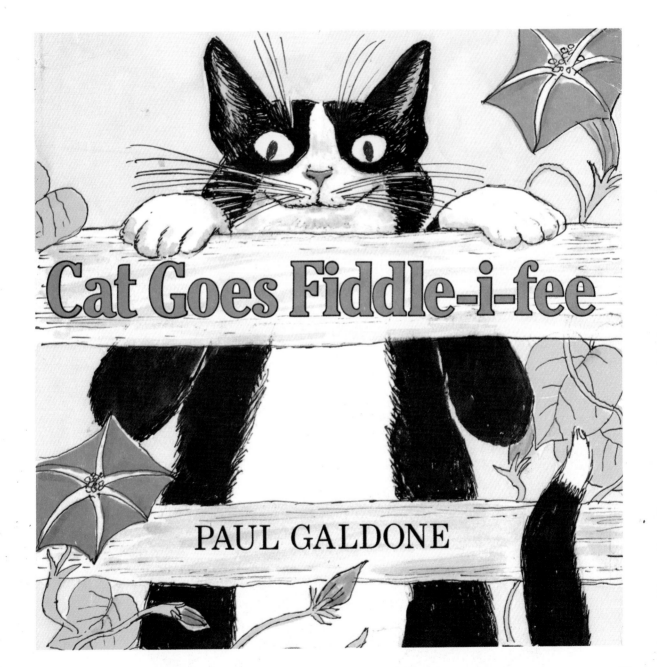

Cat Goes Fiddle-i-fee

PAUL GALDONE

I had a cat and the cat pleased me,
I fed my cat by yonder tree.
Cat goes fiddle-i-fee.

I had a hen and the hen pleased me,
I fed my hen by yonder tree.
Hen goes chimmy-chuck, chimmy-chuck,
Cat goes fiddle-i-fee.

10

I had a duck and the duck pleased me,
I fed my duck by yonder tree.
Duck goes quack, quack,
Hen goes chimmy-chuck, chimmy-chuck,
Cat goes fiddle-i-fee.

I had a goose and the goose pleased me,
I fed my goose by yonder tree.
Goose goes swishy, swashy,
Duck goes quack, quack,
Hen goes chimmy-chuck, chimmy-chuck,
Cat goes fiddle-i-fee.

I had a sheep and the sheep pleased me,
I fed my sheep by yonder tree.
Sheep goes baa, baa,
Goose goes swishy, swashy,
Duck goes quack, quack,
Hen goes chimmy-chuck, chimmy-chuck,
Cat goes fiddle-i-fee.

I had a pig and the pig pleased me,
I fed my pig by yonder tree.
Pig goes griffy, gruffy,
Sheep goes baa, baa,
Goose goes swishy, swashy,
Duck goes quack, quack,
Hen goes chimmy-chuck, chimmy-chuck,
Cat goes fiddle-i-fee.

19

I had a cow and the cow pleased me,
I fed my cow by yonder tree.
Cow goes moo, moo,
Pig goes griffy, gruffy,
Sheep goes baa, baa,
Goose goes swishy, swashy,
Duck goes quack, quack,
Hen goes chimmy-chuck, chimmy-chuck,
Cat goes fiddle-i-fee.

I had a horse and the horse pleased me,
I fed my horse by yonder tree.
Horse goes neigh, neigh,
Cow goes moo, moo,
Pig goes griffy, gruffy,
Sheep goes baa, baa,
Goose goes swishy, swashy,
Duck goes quack, quack,
Hen goes chimmy-chuck, chimmy-chuck,
Cat goes fiddle-i-fee.

23

I had a dog and the dog pleased me,
I fed my dog by yonder tree.
Dog goes bow-wow, bow-wow,
Horse goes neigh, neigh,
Cow goes moo, moo,
Pig goes griffy, gruffy,
Sheep goes baa, baa,
Goose goes swishy, swashy,
Duck goes quack, quack,
Hen goes chimmy-chuck, chimmy-chuck,
Cat goes fiddle-i-fee.

Then Grandma came
and she fed me . . .

while the others dozed
by yonder tree.

And cat went fiddle-i-fee.

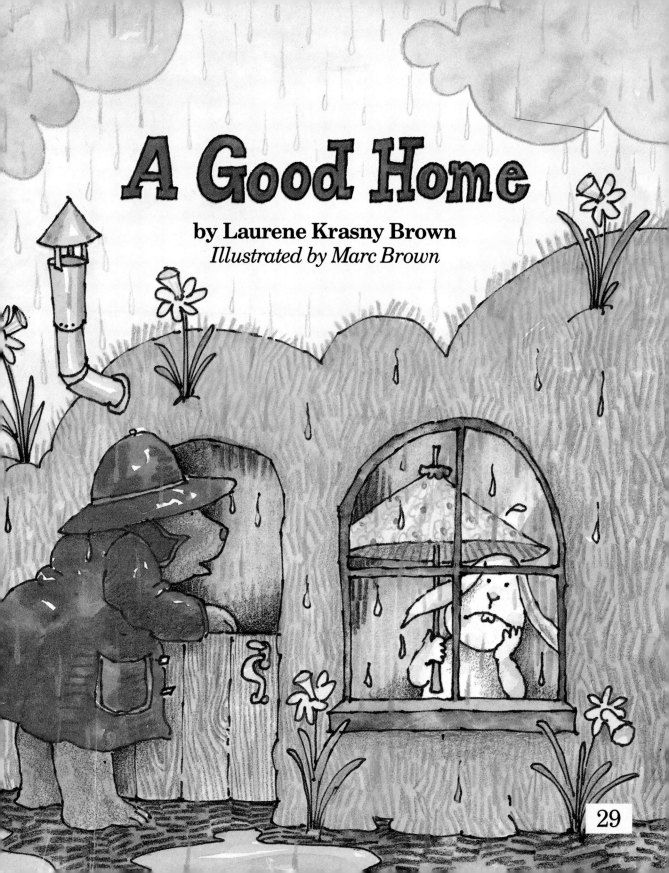

A Good Home

by Laurene Krasny Brown

Illustrated by Marc Brown

One day,
Bear went to see Rabbit.

"I need a new home!" said Rabbit.

"No, you don't," said Bear.

"Yes, I do," said Rabbit. "And
Turtle can help me."

So Rabbit went to see Turtle.
Bear went, too.

"Hello!" said Turtle. "What can
I do for you?"

"Please help me," said Rabbit.
"I need a new home!"

"I know just the home for you,"
said Turtle. "I can show it to you now."

"Good!" said Rabbit. "Take me to it."

Good
Homes

31

"Here we are," said Turtle.

"What a big home," said Bear.

"It's <u>too</u> big!" said Rabbit. "Do you have other homes to show me, Turtle?"

"I know just the home for you," Turtle said. "I can show it to you now."

"Good!" said Rabbit. "Take me to it!"

"Here we are," said Turtle.

"What a little home," said Bear.

"It's <u>too</u> little!" said Rabbit.

"I know just the home for you,"
Turtle said. "I can show it to you now."

"Good!" said Rabbit. "Take me to it!"

"Here we are," said Turtle.

"Now this is a good home!" said Bear.

"It may be good for a bear,"
said Rabbit, "but not for a rabbit!
Show me other homes, Turtle! Please!"

"I can't," said Turtle. "I have
no other homes to show you!"

34

Then Bear said, "I know just the home for you, Rabbit."

"You do, Bear?" said Rabbit.

"Yes," said Bear. "I can show it to you now."

"Take me to it, Bear!" said Rabbit.

"Take me, too," said Turtle.

"Here we are," said Bear. "It's <u>your</u> home, Rabbit. We just need to fix it!"

"What do you think, Turtle?" said Rabbit.

"Let's get to work," said Turtle. "This is just the home for you!"

"It is," said Rabbit. "Good for Bear!"

Good Morning, Chick

by Mirra Ginsburg
Illustrated by Byron Barton

There was a little house
White and smooth

like this

One morning, tap-tap and crack!
The house split open

And a chick came out.
He was small and yellow and fluffy

like this

With a yellow beak
And yellow feet

like these

His mother's name was Speckled Hen.
She looked

like this

She loved the chick
And taught him to eat worms
And seeds and crumbs,
Peck-peck, peck-peck, peck-peck

like this

A big black cat jumped out
Of the house and hissed
At the chick

like this

The Speckled Hen spread out her wings
And covered the chick like this
"Cluck-cluck-cluck!" she scolded,
And the cat backed away

like this

Then a rooster flew up on the fence,
Stretched his neck, and sang,
"Cock-a-doodle-do!"

"That's easy," said the chick.
"I can do it too."
He flapped his wings
And ran.
He stretched his neck
And opened his beak

like this

47

But all that came out
Of his beak was a tiny little
"Peep! Peep!"
He didn't look where he was going
And he fell into a puddle,
Plop!

like this

A frog sat in the puddle and laughed,
"Qua-ha! Wait till you grow
Before you can crow!"
The frog looked

like this

And the wet chick looked

like this

Now Speckled Hen ran to her chick.
She warmed and coddled him

like this

The chick dried out
And was round and golden and fluffy
again.
And off they went together
To look for worms and crumbs and
seeds.
Peck-peck, peck-peck, peck-peck

like this

A Kite

I often sit and wish that I
Could be a kite up in the sky,
And ride upon the breeze and go
Whichever way I chanced to blow.

Anonymous

Boo Bear
and the Kite

Written and Illustrated by
David McPhail

Boo had a new kite.

"I like your new kite," said Pig.
"But I want to see it fly."

"OK," said Boo. "Here I go!"

Boo ran and ran and ran.
Then he ran some more.
But the kite wouldn't fly!

"This kite won't fly!" said Boo.

"I'll get your kite to fly," said Pig.
"Look out! Here I go!"

Pig ran and ran and ran.
Then he ran some more.
But the kite wouldn't fly!

"This kite won't fly," said Pig.
"This just isn't a good day to fly
a kite!"

"Oh, no!" said Boo. "I wanted to
see it fly."

Then Fox came by.

"Hello, Boo. Hello, Pig," said Fox.
"I see you have a kite. This is
a good day to fly a kite."

"It's not a good day for _my_ kite,"
said Boo. "It won't fly!"

"I know what you need," said Fox.
"You need a big tail."

Boo and Pig looked at their tails.

"I have a tail," said Pig. "But it's very little."

"My tail is little, too," said Boo.

"Now I see!" said Pig. "We don't have big tails! That's why we can't fly your kite, Boo!"

"Fox, you have a big tail," said Boo.
"You can fly the kite."

"Yes, <u>you</u> fly it," said Pig.

"No, no, no!" said Fox. "It's the kite
that needs a big tail!"

Fox helped Boo and Pig make
the kite tail.

"So this is a kite tail!" said Boo.

Fox said, "Now try to fly
your kite, Boo."

"Look out! Here I go!" said Boo, and
he ran with the kite.

"The tail works," said Pig.

"Look at my kite go!" said Boo.
"It is a good day to fly a kite!"

OVER IN THE MEADOW

Illustrated by Ezra Jack Keats

Over in the meadow,
In the sand, in the sun,
Lived an old mother turtle
And her little turtle one.

"Dig!" said the mother.
"I dig," said the one.
So he dug all day,
In the sand, in the sun.

Over in the meadow,
Where the stream runs blue,
Lived an old mother fish
And her little fishes two.

"Swim!" said the mother.
"We swim," said the two.
So they swam and they leaped,
Where the stream runs blue.

Over in the meadow,
In a hole in a tree,
Lived a mother bluebird
And her little birdies three.

"Sing!" said the mother.
"We sing," said the three.
So they sang and were glad,
In the hole in the tree.

Over in the meadow,
In the reeds on the shore,
Lived a mother muskrat
And her little ratties four.

"Dive!" said the mother.
"We dive," said the four.
So they dived and they burrowed,
In the reeds on the shore.

Over in the meadow,
In a snug beehive,
Lived a mother honeybee
And her little honeys five.

"Buzz!" said the mother.
"We buzz," said the five.
 So they buzzed and they hummed,
 Near the snug beehive.

Over in the meadow
In a nest built of sticks
Lived a black mother crow
And her little crows six.

"Caw!" said the mother.
"We caw," said the six.
So they cawed and they called,
In their nest built of sticks.

Over in the meadow,
Where the grass is so even,
Lived a gay mother cricket
And her little crickets seven.

"Chirp!" said the mother.
"We chirp," said the seven.
So they chirped cheery notes,
In the grass soft and even.

Over in the meadow,
By the old mossy gate,
Lived a brown mother lizard
And her little lizards eight.

"Bask!" said the mother.
"We bask," said the eight.
So they basked in the sun,
By the old mossy gate.

Over in the meadow,
Where the clear pools shine,
Lived a green mother frog
And her little froggies nine.

"Croak!" said the mother.
"We croak," said the nine.
So they croaked and they jumped,
Where the clear pools shine.

Over in the meadow,
In a soft shady glen,
Lived a mother firefly
And her little flies ten.

"Shine!" said the mother.
"We shine," said the ten.
So they shone like stars,
In the soft, shady glen.

THE LITTLE TURTLE

There was a little turtle.
He lived in a box.
He swam in a puddle.
He climbed on the rocks.

He snapped at a mosquito.
He snapped at a flea.
He snapped at a minnow.
And he snapped at me.

He caught the mosquito.
He caught the flea.
He caught the minnow.
But he didn't catch me.

Vachel Lindsay

"Good day, Little Rabbit," said Fox.
"Can a frog get some lunch here?"

"A frog can get a good lunch here,"
said Little Rabbit. "Are you a frog?"

Fox said, "Don't I look like a frog?"

"You look like a frog to me,"
said Little Rabbit. "You look like
a big red frog."

"May I please come in for my lunch?"
asked Fox.

"I have to see," said Little Rabbit.
"I'll tell Mother that you are here.
She will make your lunch."

Fox was not pleased. But he said,
"OK, Little Rabbit. That will do for now."

Little Rabbit went to Mother Rabbit.
"Mother," she said. "A big red frog
wants to come in."

"A <u>red</u> frog?" said Mother Rabbit.

"Yes, Mother," said Little Rabbit.
"A big red frog. He wants to come in
for some lunch."

"Frogs aren't red!" said Mother.
"Tell me, Little Rabbit. Did that frog
have a tail?"

"Yes, Mother," said Little Rabbit.
"A big red tail."

"Little Rabbit!" said Mother.
"That's not a frog! That's a fox!"

"A FOX!" said Little Rabbit.
"Help! Help! What can we do?
That fox wants <u>us</u> for lunch!"

"We'll fix that fox!" said Mother.
"He'll get lunch, but it won't be
rabbits!"

"Hello, Frog," said Mother Rabbit. "Here's your lunch."

"May I please come in?" asked Fox.

"No, you may not," said Mother Rabbit. "You may have your lunch out here."

Fox was not pleased.

Mother Rabbit watched Fox.
"Do you like it?" she asked.

"It's a very good lunch," said Fox.
"What is it?"

"It's what frogs like for lunch,"
said Mother Rabbit.

"And what is that?" asked Fox.

"It's fly soup," said Mother Rabbit.

"Fly soup?" said Fox. "FLY SOUP!"

"Yes," said Mother Rabbit. "Would you like some more?"

"No! No! No!" said Fox. "I would not like some more!"

"Your fly soup did it, Mother!"
said Little Rabbit. "Look at that
Fox go!"

OH,
A-HUNTING
WE WILL GO

John Langstaff
pictures by
Nancy Winslow Parker

Houghton Mifflin Literature

Sometimes you read a story again and again because it's fun to say the words. The stories you have read are like that. And so is *A-Hunting We Will Go!*